# Letterland

## Phonics Practice 5

24 pages

Decodable text

**Contains:**
ar, or, (ore, oor, our)
er, ir, ur, wr, -ve,
o (as in son), oo (as in book),
u (as in put)

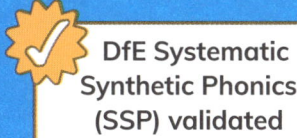

DfE Systematic Synthetic Phonics (SSP) validated

Name:

**Arthur Ar, the apple stealer**

**ar** as in f**ar**m

1. Arthur Ar is stealing apples. Read the words, then join each word to the matching picture. Write the words again.

scarf

car

shark

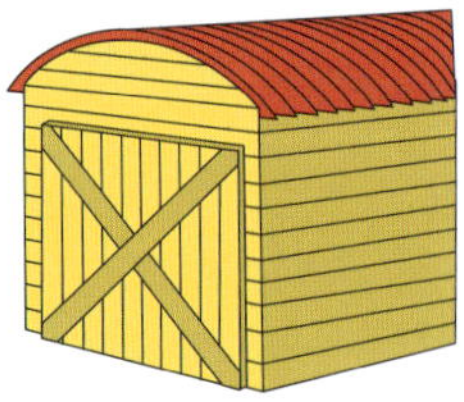

barn

dark

scarf

2. Read the clue and write an **ar** word.

1. A place to play with swings and slides.

_____

2. A place to put hay to dry.

_____

3. Be a Word Detective and catch Arthur Ar stealing apples. Read the story. Then draw a circle around every **ar**. There are fourteen to find.

It is dark, and Arthur Ar cannot find his radar car. Is it in the farmyard? Did he park it in the barn? He trips on his scarf. A dog barks, and the alarm on his car starts!

4. Write over the word that makes sense in the sentences below.

1. My dog likes to  bark / lark  at cars.

2. When it gets  shark / dark  we can see Mars.

3. Write your name in the  March / card .

4. Stepping on plants may  hard / harm  them.

Orvil Or, the orange stealer

**or** as in for

1. Orvil Or is stealing oranges. Read the words, then join each word to the matching picture. Write the words again.

fork

storm

shorts

north

sport

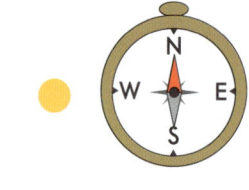

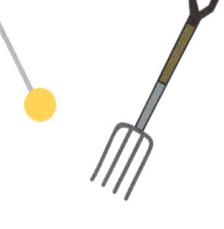

2. Read the sentence.
Then write a new sentence using some of the other words.

| has | he | she | corn | on | a | fork | sport | for | stork | Friday |

She has corn on a fork.

4

3. Even with a Magic e on the end, Orvil Or still says his last name. Write **ore** to complete these words. Read them and match them to the pictures.

sc_ore_

sn____

sh____

s____

4. Be a Word Detective and catch Orvil Or stealing oranges. Read the story. Then draw a circle around every **or**. There are fifteen to find.

Orvil Or is on his boat this morning with corn for his horse. A storm from the north is on the way. He must get to the shore, but his short arms feel sore. Will Orvil Or make it to a safe port, or not?

**Revision - ar, or**

1. Listen for a robot saying his last name in these words. Write the correct pair of letters in the spaces: **ar** or **or**.

c**ar**d     c__n     st__rt

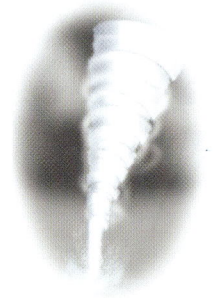  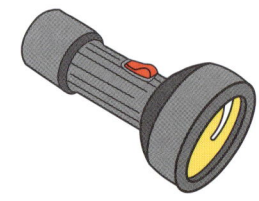

st__m     b__k     t__ch

2. Write the words in the box under the words that rhyme. Then read the rhyming lists to a friend.

| smart | yard | jar | bark | start | far |
| shark | hard | cart | park | star |

| part | car | dark | card |
| smart | | | |

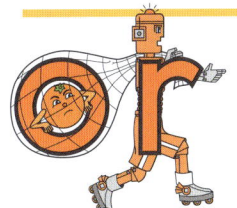

3. Orvil Or sometimes captures more than one vowel. He almost always reports back with his last name, 'Or'. Sort and write the words below by spelling patterns.

| store | door | more | your |
| floor | poor | four | core | pour |

_store_

4. Read the sentence. The missing words start with the Letterlander's sound. Write an **ar** or **or**, or **oor** word in the space.

1. Munching Mike can see _____ in the dark sky.

2. Is that Dippy Duck behind the _____ ?

3. Sammy Snake's pal is sticking _____ on a card.

7

Ernest Er, the elephant stealer

**er** as in her

1. Ernest Er is stealing elephants. Read the words, then join each word to the matching picture. Write the words again.

numbers

letters         **1 2 3**     scarf

ladder

dinner

runner

2. Write the words in the spaces to complete this sentence.

| sister   summer   winter |

My _____ likes the _____ .

Ernest Er prefers the _____ .

3. Sort and write the words in the box into the correct groups. Some may fit in more than one group.

| panther | farmer | golfer | hamster |
| painter | waiter | singer | swimmer |
| archer | | cleaner | runner |
| teacher | | butterfly | otter |

**Sports person**

_____

_____

_____

**Animals**

_____

_____

_____

_____

_____

**Jobs**

_____

_____

_____    _____

_____

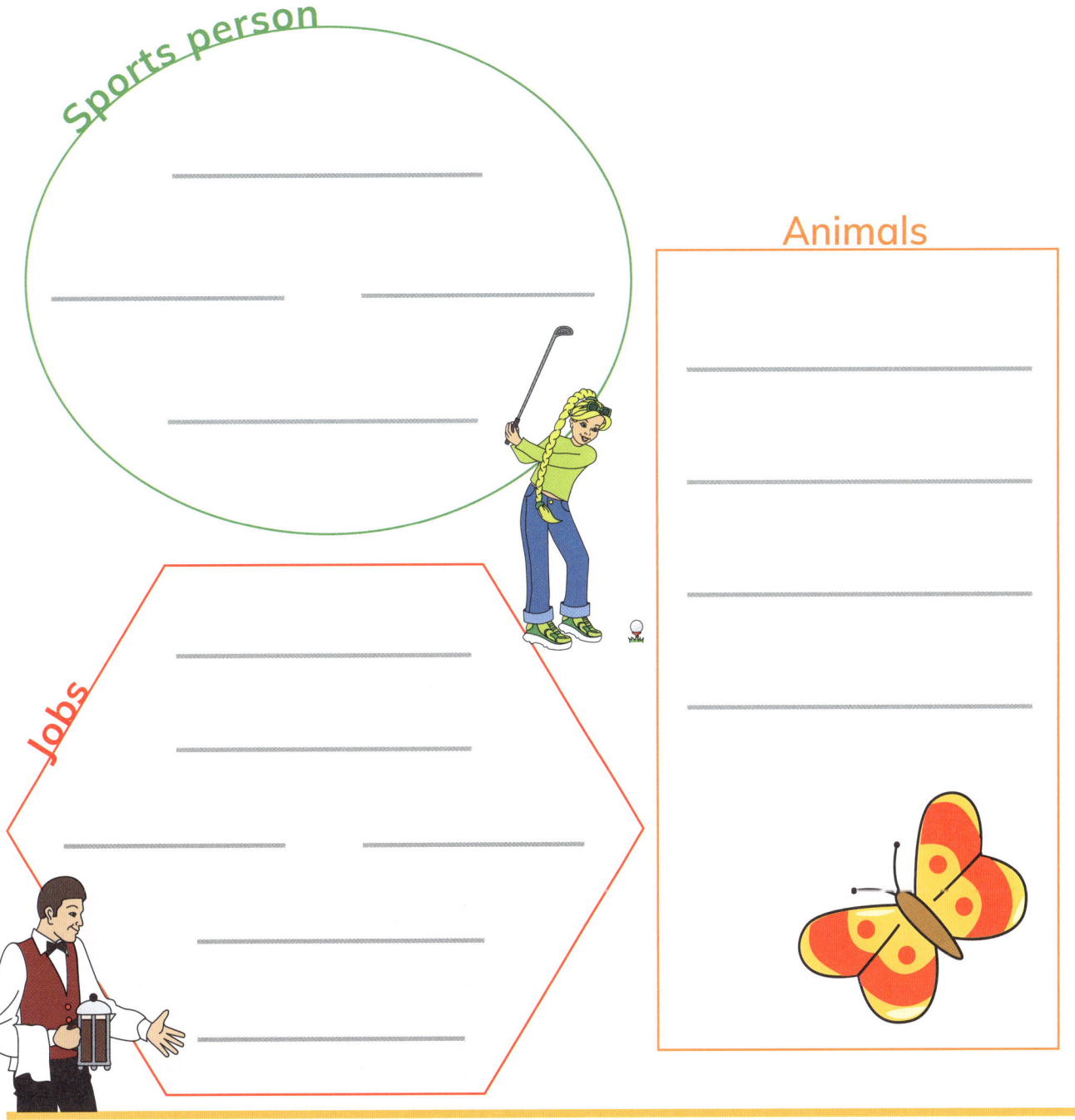

Irving Ir, the ink stealer

**ir** as in girl

1. Irving Ir is stealing ink bottles. Read the words, then join each word to the matching picture. Write the words again.

bird

girl

shirt           bird

dirt

skirt

2. Read the sentence.
Then write a new sentence using some of the other words.

| red | a | has | bird | shirt | man | skirt | dirty | girl | the |

The girl has a red bird.

10

3. Be a Word Detective and catch Irving Ir stealing ink. Read the story. Then draw a circle around every **ir**. There are thirteen to find.

Irving Ir always tries to run off with ink. Impy Ink squirts ink on the robot's shirt. His first, third, thirteenth and thirty-third shirts are dirty. Can you catch Irving thirteen times in this story?

4. These Letterlanders are coming out to play a game. Label the first and third out of the gate.

Urgent Ur, the umbrella stealer

**ur** as in fur

1. Urgent Ur is stealing umbrellas. Read the words, then join each word to the matching picture. Write the words again.

surf

purse     surf

nurse

burn

curl

2. Match the phrase to the picture and write it below.

burning twigs      a hurting leg      a lurking fox

3. Be a Word Detective and catch Urgent Ur stealing umbrellas. Read the story. Then draw a circle around every **ur**. There are fourteen to find.

"It hurts!" says Urgent Ur to the nurse. Urgent Ur had tripped on the curb trying to grab an umbrella.

The nurse turned. "It will stop hurting on Thursday. Until then, curl up Urgent Ur."

4. Read the sentence. Write one of these words in the space.

| burn | disturb | nurse | turns |

1. The flame is hot. It will _____ .

2. We must not _____ that bird's nest.

3. We take _____ on the swings.

4. When I am hurt the _____ helps.

# Review - er, ir, ur

1. Write the word for each picture. The robot at the top of each column tells you which brother is in the word.

| er | ir | ur |
|---|---|---|
|  |  |  |
| 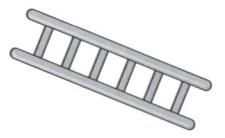 |  |  |
|  |  |  |
|  |  |  |
|  |  |  |

2. Put these puzzle pieces together to make four longer words to write on the lines below.

surf · ther
fur · er

squirt · der
or · er

_____   _____

_____   _____

3. It is Bouncy Ben's birthday. These are his presents. Write the words on the labels.

| birthday card | blue shirt |
| birthday cake | big computer |

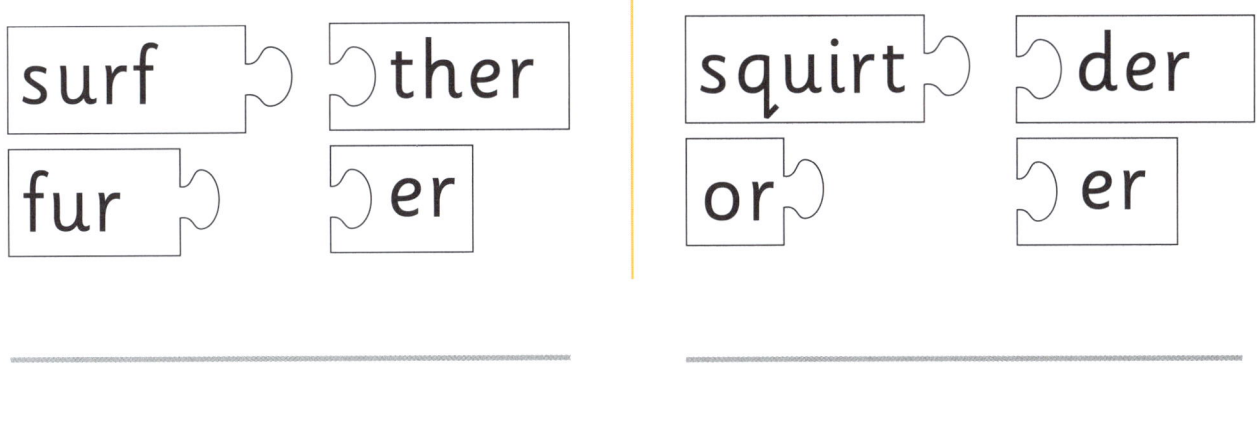

15

Walter Walrus captures Red Robot

**wr** as in write

1. Complete the sentences using the words below. Cross out the word that is **wrong**.

wrap   writes   wreck

She likes to _____ gifts.

She _____ names on the tags.

2. Which gift has been given the **wrong** label? Circle it, then complete the sentence using the words below.

Ben   Fred   Vicky

I _____ on the tag but I got the name _____ .

wrote   wrong

3. Draw a line around all the **wr** words in the word search below. They go across and down.

| w | r | a | p | o | z | t |
|---|---|---|---|---|---|---|
| a | e | w | r | e | c | k |
| l | s | r | t | x | a | w |
| n | o | i | y | l | i | r |
| p | u | t | s | r | b | i |
| t | a | e | m | p | o | n |
| s | f | w | r | o | n | g |

write

wreck

wrap

wring

Can you find one more **wr** word in the grid?
Copy it on to the lines.

_____ _____ _____

4. Read the sentence and match it to the picture clue.

This wren has got a wrapper! •

This wren has got his dinner! •

Vase Prop e

**-ve** as in have

1. Match the sentences to the pictures.

I like olives!

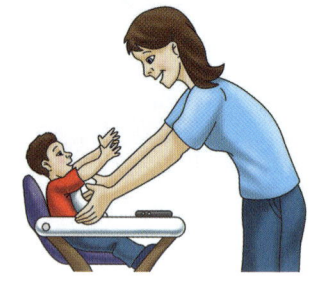

I have a cup.

I live with mum.

Give me a hug.

2. Now write your own two sentences using the words below.

have   live   give

# o as in son

Oscar's Bothersome Little Brother

1. Read the words. Listen to the vowel sounds in the middle. Join each word to Oscar Orange or his Bothersome Brother.

son    fog

come    rock

love    pop

log    some

2. Write in the missing words to finish the sentences to match the picture.

| some   love   son   come |

We have a _____ .

We have _____ to pick him up.

We _____ him.

19

The Boot and Foot Twins

**oo** as in book

1. Link oo to the words that contain their sound. Write the words in the spaces. Cross out the other pictures.

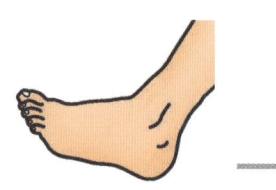

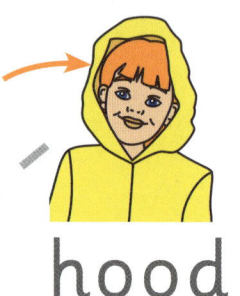

hood

2. Read the sentences and write one of these words in the spaces.

| took   hood   cooked   shook |

The girl _____ a cake from the tray.

The food has not been _____.

The man shivered and _____.

The rain fell on her _____.

3. Put these puzzle pieces together to make three longer words to write on the lines below.

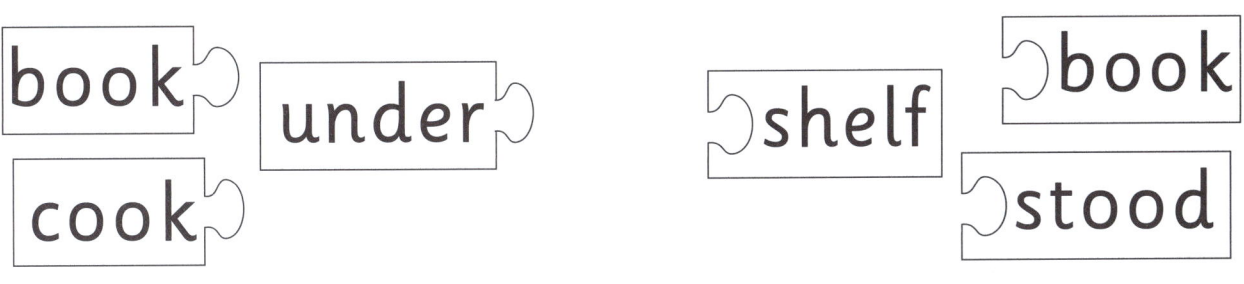

_____

_____    _____

4. Fill in the missing words to complete the sentence.

Five, good _____

on a bookshelf made of _____ .

5. Match the sounds of oo with the Boot or Foot Twin. Write the words in the spaces.

food   cook   soon   good   took   smooth   zoo   wood

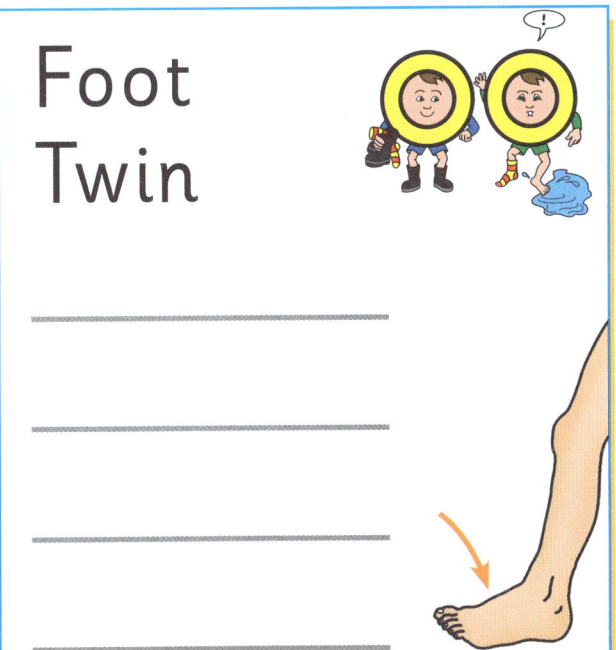

 Upside Down Umbrella  u as in put

1. Write the word for each picture. Then write the word that rhymes below each one.

push    pull    bull    bush

_____     _____

_____     _____

2. Read the sentences and write one of these words in the spaces.

push   pull   bull   full   put

The farmer told us that the barn is _____ so we have to _____ and _____ the _____. We can _____ it in a shed.

3. Read the sentences. Then colour the star next to the matching picture.

The cup is full.

Is that bird in the bush a cuckoo?

The butcher shop is open.

He likes pudding!

4. Look at the picture and fill in the words. Read the instructions out loud.

"Ben, _____ on Peter!"

"Peter, _____ on Clever Cat!"

"Clever Cat, _____ on the carrot!"

# How to use this book

On each page, read the instructions to the children. Discuss the pictures, as needed. Let them try and read all the words in the exercises themselves, as they are decodable.

**Further vowel sounds and spellings**
The workbooks are designed to consolidate and extend the teaching content of the *Letterland Phonics Teacher's Guide,* in which the story logic for r-controlled vowels is introduced as well as other vowel sounds and spellings.

Skills covered include:
- phonemic awareness
- decoding skills
- word building
- reading for meaning
- sentence completion
- using words in context when writing
- open-ended sentence writing.

It is important to use this workbook:
- when children are not tired
- when there are no background distractions
- for short periods of time
- with plenty of praise and encouragement.

## Correct handwriting positions

### Left-hander

Fingertips 4cm from tip of pencil

Paper side edge 30°
Table edge

Elbows off the table
Feet on floor

### Right-hander

Paper side edge 20°
Table edge

Chair slightly tilted
Feet on floor

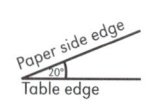
Fingertips 2cm from tip of pencil

---

Published by Letterland International Ltd.
8/10 South Street, Epsom, Surrey, KT18 7PF, UK
© Letterland International 2021
10 9 8 7 6 5 4 3 2

ISBN: 978-1-78248-555-1
Product Code: TP69

LETTERLAND™ is a trademark of Letterland International Ltd.
Printed in China.

All rights reserved. No part of this publication may be reproduced, stored in a retrieval system, or transmitted in any form or by any means, electronic, mechanical, photocopying, recording or otherwise, without the prior permission of the Publisher or a licence permitting restricted copying in the United Kingdom issued by the Copyright Licensing Agency Ltd, 90 Tottenham Court Road, London W1P 0LP, British Library Cataloguing in Publication Data. A catalogue record for this book is available from the British Library.

Sassoon Infant is a typeface designed for children learning to read and write.
© Adrian Williams Design Ltd

Written and designed by Lisa Holt
Consultant: Lyn Wendon, originator of Letterland

## You may also like:

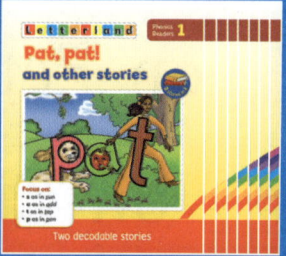
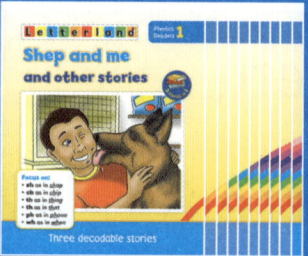

See our full range at: **www.letterland.com**

Please Note: These practice books match the teaching order in the Letterland *Phonics Teacher's Guide.*

For those who wish to follow a different teaching order the practice books can be used flexibly.

Code: TP69
ISBN 978-1-78248-555-1

9 781782 485551

Letterland Child-friendly phonics